Teacher Resource

PHONICS ACTIVITIES 2

Consonant Blends, Long Vowels and Specials Vowels

BRIGHTER™
VISION

Brighter Vision Education Ltd.,
Eton House, 18-24 Paradise Road, Richmond, Surrey TW9 1SR

Copyright 1996 Brighter Vision Education Ltd.

™ is a trademark of Brighter Vision Education Ltd.

Some material used in this book is used under licence from
Frank Schaffer Publications Inc.

Consultant Editor: Pam Hutchinson

Printed in Belgium
Reprinted 1998

BV-05-302 Teacher Resource Key Stage 1/P1-P3: Phonics Activities 2
ISBN 1 86172 023 8

INTRODUCTION

This set of 99 phonics activity sheets has been designed to support and consolidate the development of your pupils' listening, reading and writing skills.

To enable you to select appropriate material for your class and for individual pupils, the activities are grouped as follows:

★ consonant blends
★ short vowel consolidation a
★ short vowel consolidation e
★ short vowel consolidation i
★ short vowel consolidation o
★ long vowels
★ vowels and blends review
★ special vowels

The detailed contents list gives a short description of each activity and there is sufficient reinforcement of consonant blends and long and short vowels to ensure that, however much practice pupils may need, it will be varied and enjoyable.

Give your pupils the firm foundation they need by using selected, appropriate activities from the book. Should they need further practice in consonant and short vowels, use Phonics Activities 1 in this series.

CONTENTS

Say the name of the picture.
Write the blend you hear at the beginning of it.

_____ove   _____ant   _____ide

1

Phonics

Colour the pictures in each row that begin with the blend at the beginning of the row.

gl			
pl			
sl			
gl			
pl			
sl			

Phonics

Say the name of the picture.
Write the blend you hear at the beginning of it.

_ _ _ _ _ **ock**   _ _ _ _ _ **own**   _ _ _ _ _ **ower**

3

Colour the pictures in each row that begin with the blend at the beginning of the row.

bl			
cl			
fl			
bl			
cl			
fl			

4

Phonics

Name _____

Print the answer to each riddle on the correct flag.
Use the words in the cloud to help you.

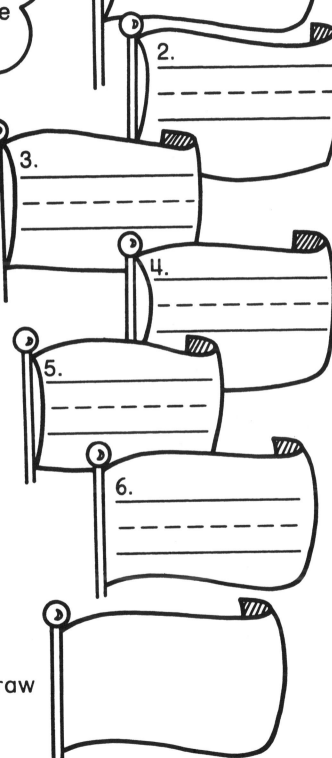

plum glass clock
blue   float flame

1. I help you tell the time.

2. I am a colour.

3. You can eat me.

4. I am hot.

5. A boat can do this.

6. You can put water in me.

Use the flag at the bottom to draw
your country's flag.

5

Phonics

Say the name of the picture.
Circle the blend you hear at the beginning of it.

bl	sl	gl	pl	fl	bl	gl	cl	sl	cl	sl	pl

pl	gl	cl	fl	sl	gl	gl	fl	sl	pl	fl	cl

fl	pl	sl	sl	cl	gl	sl	cl	pl	sl	gl	cl

sl	bl	pl	sl	pl	bl	fl	gl	sl	pl	bl	pl

6

Phonics

Say the name of the picture.
Write the blend you hear at the beginning of it.

og ———— apes ———— ize ———— ee

7

Phonics

Colour the pictures in each row that begin with the blend at
the beginning of the row.

fr			
gr			
pr			
tr			
gr			
pr			

8

Phonics

Say the name of the picture.
Write the blend you hear at the beginning of it.

br **cr** **dr**

__ __ ush   __ __ ayon   __ __ agon

Phonics

Colour the pictures in each row that begin with the blend at the beginning of the row.

br			
cr			
dr			
br			
cr			
dr			

Phonics

Say the name of the picture.
Circle the blend you hear at the beginning of it.

br	dr	cr	fr	pr	tr	pr	gr	cr	cr	gr	tr

fr	gr	pr	br	dr	cr	fr	dr	tr	cr	dr	br

br	tr	cr	gr	tr	pr	fr	br	dr	fr	dr	tr

cr	dr	pr	gr	cr	br	pr	tr	br	gr	tr	br

11

Phonics

Look at the picture in each raindrop.
Then print the missing blend on the umbrella

1. [ ] [ ] o g   6. [ ] [ ] u m

2. [ ] [ ] a b   7. [ ] [ ] i z e

3. [ ] [ ] u c k   8. [ ] [ ] o s s

4. [ ] [ ] i c k   9. [ ] [ ] e s s

5. [ ] [ ] a p e s   10. [ ] [ ] e e

12

Phonics

Name _____

brag   blow   drip
brim   drum   drag
blob   drop

These look tricky!

Fill in the blanks with words.

1	Beat the _____.
2	See the tap _____.
3	Don't _____.
4	It's full to the _____.
5	I put on a _____ of paste.

13

     Phonics

grin	glad	play
grip	glow	plum
grab	plug	

Fill in the blanks with words.

1	Let's _____ tag.
2	I will eat this _____.
3	Please_____ it in.
4	Look at that cat _____.
5	I am _____ you are here.

14

Phonics

flag   frog   trip
flat   from   trim
flap   trap

Fill in the blanks with words.

1	Now _____ your wings.
2	Look out for the _____!
3	It's a letter _____ Grandma!
4	Look out for a _____.
5	This is our school_____.

15

clip	club	crib
clap	claw	crow
clam	crab	

Fill in the blanks with words.

1	Suzy is in her _____.
2	Look at that _____.
3	I _____ Max every month.
4	I found a _____.
5	Here is a _____ shell.

16

Name _____

Say the name of the picture.
Write the blend you hear at the beginning of it.

17

Phonics

Colour the pictures in each row that begin with the blend at the beginning of the row.

sp	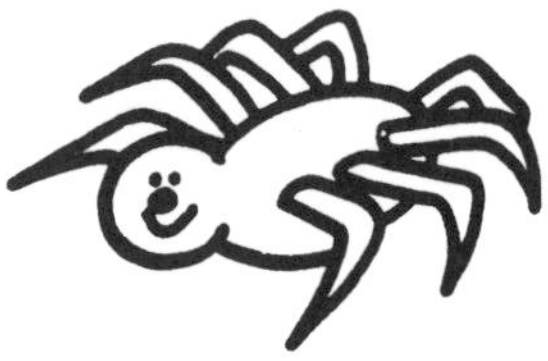	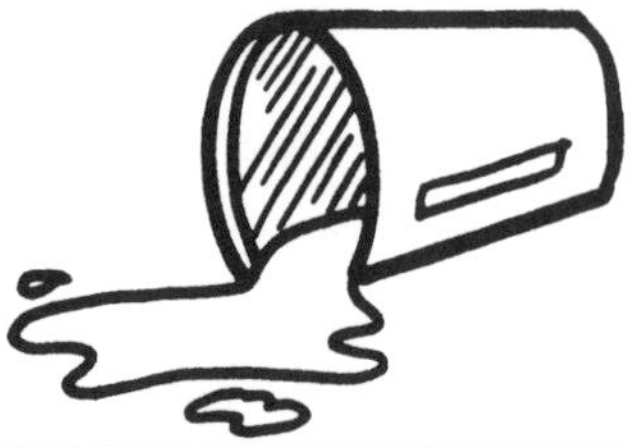	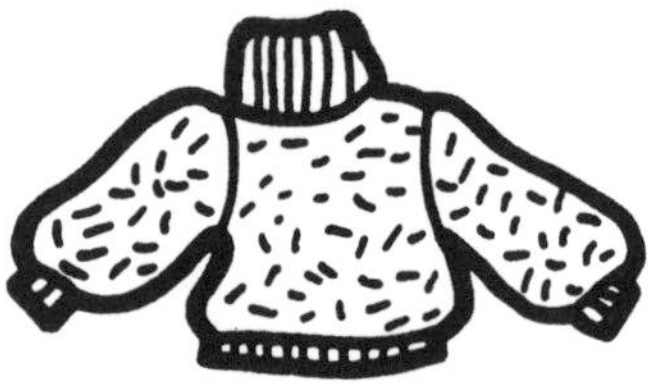
st	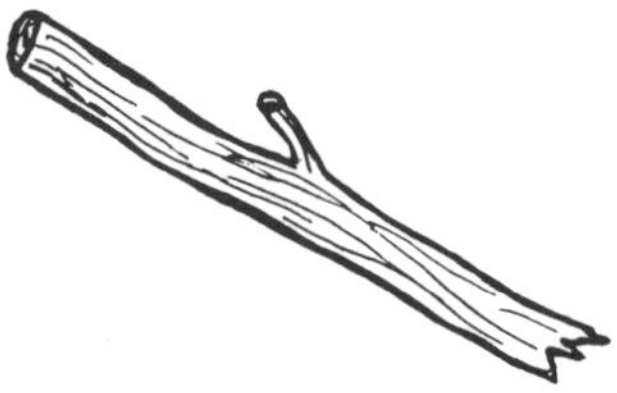	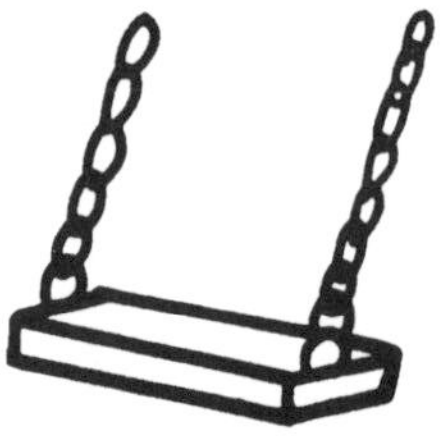	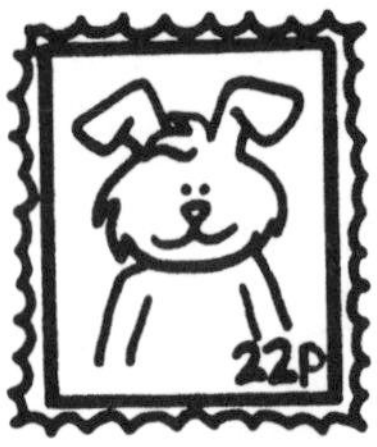
sw	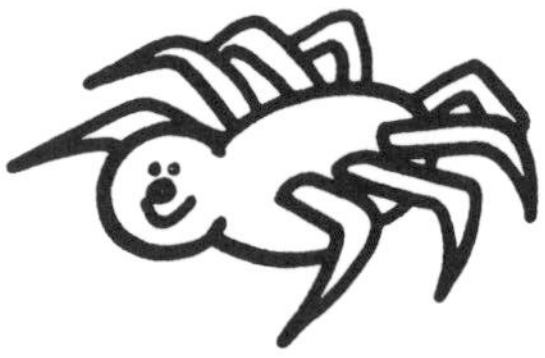	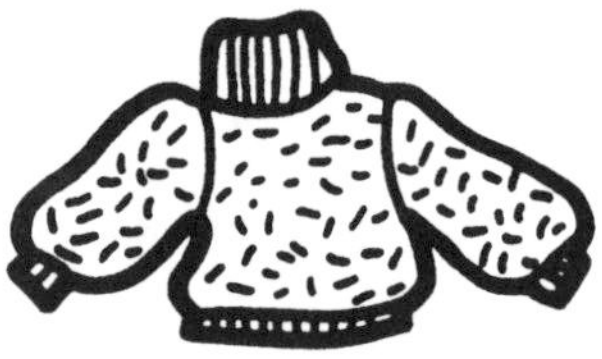	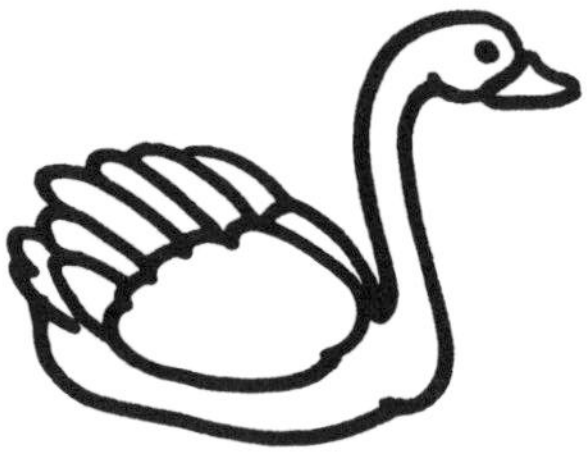
sp	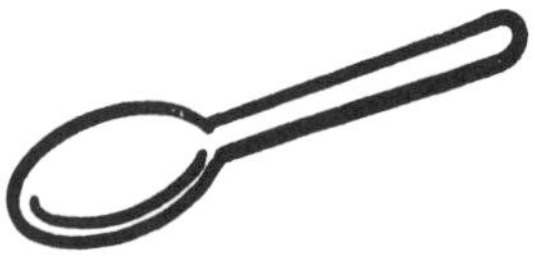	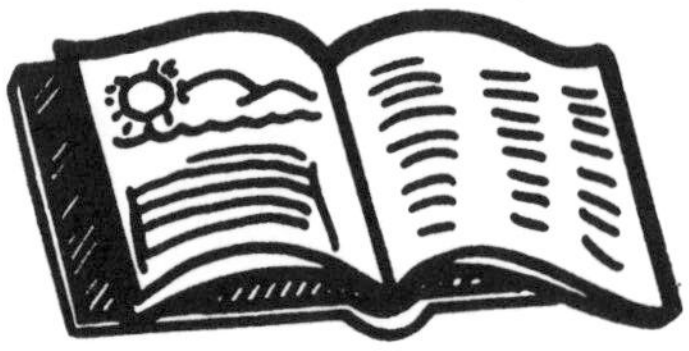	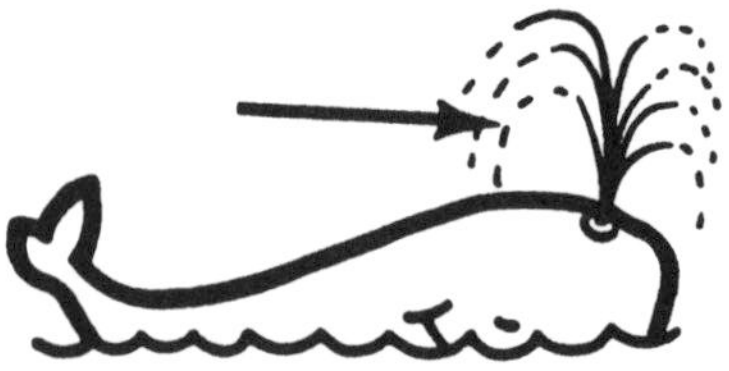
st	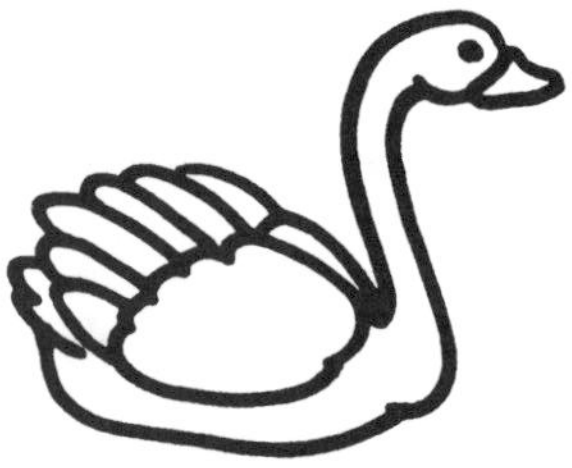	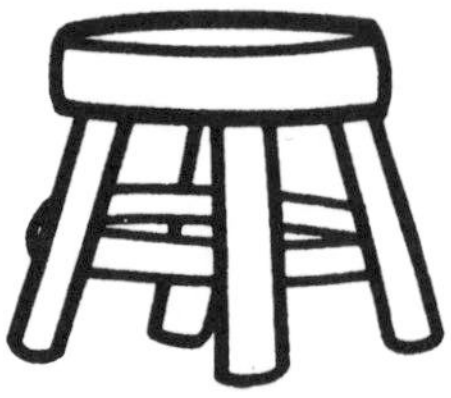	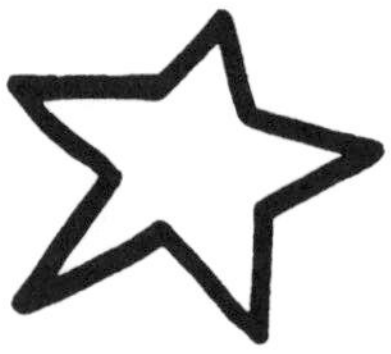
sw	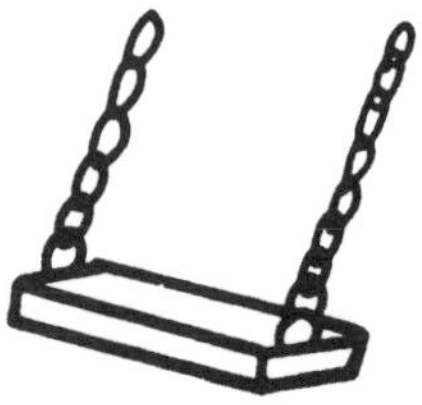	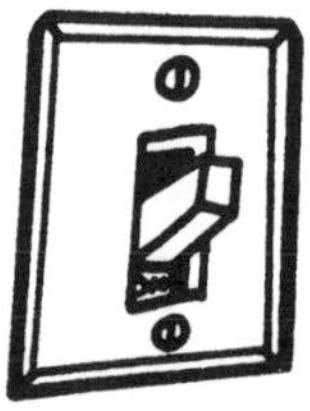	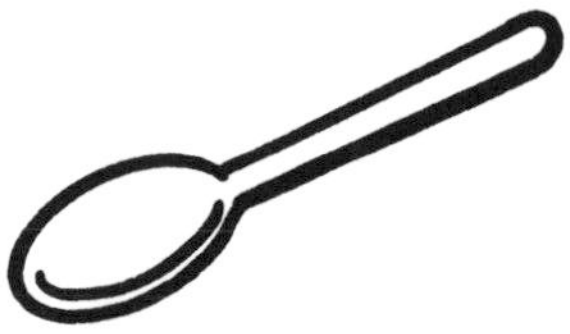

18

Phonics

Say the name of the picture.
Write the blend you hear at the beginning of it.

_____unk   _____ake   _____oon

Phonics

Colour the pictures in each row that begin with the blend at the beginning of the row.

sk			
sn			
sp			
sk			
sn			
sp			

Phonics

Say the name of the picture.
Circle the blend you hear at the beginning of it.

sp	sw	st	sp	sw	sn	st	sn	sp	sw	sp	st

st	sp	sn	sw	sp	st	sw	sp	sn	st	sp	sn

sn	sp	sw	st	sn	sw	sw	sp	st	sp	sn	st

sw	sn	st	sp	sw	st	st	sp	sn	sn	sp	sw

21

Phonics

stir	snap	skip
stab	snug	skin
snip	snow	

Fill in the blanks with words.

1	I love the _____.
2	_____ the batter.
3	I am _____ in bed.
4	_____ a small piece off.
5	We like to _____ .

22

Phonics

Say the name of the picture.
Write the blend you hear at the beginning of it.

_____ ates   _____ ide   _____ oke

23

Phonics

Colour the pictures in each row that begin with the blend at the beginning of the row.

sc			
sl			
sm			
sc			
sl			
sm			

24

Phonics

Name _____

Say the name of the picture.
Circle the blend you hear at the beginning of it.

sl | sm | sk	sm | sc | sn	sl | sm | sk	sm | sc | sk
sl | sc | sm	sl | sk | sm	sk | sc | sm	sm | sk | sl
sm | sc | sk	sl | sc | sm	sk | sl | sm	sk | sc | sl
sm | sk | sl	sc | sm | sl	sm | sk | sl	sk | sm | sc

25

Phonics

Print the name of each picture in the spider's web.
Use the words at the bottom of the page.

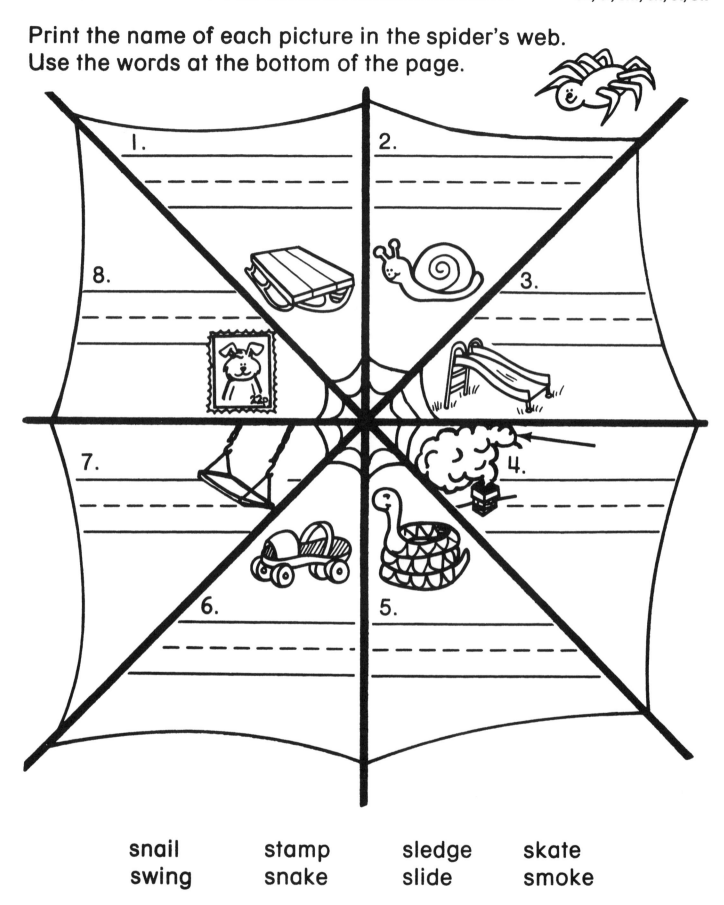

1.

2.

8.

3.

7.

4.

6.

5.

snail   stamp   sledge   skate
swing   snake   slide   smoke

Phonics

Name _____

slip   slam   star
slim   sledge stop
slap   step

Fill in the blanks with words.

1	Look at the _____.
2	Don't _____ the door!
3	A red light means _____.
4	This is my new _____.
5	The peel made her _____.

27

KS2

Name _____

Say the name of the picture.
Circle the blend you hear at the beginning of it.

gl fl sl	sw sn cr	fr br pr	sn sw cr
cr sw sn	fr cl br	sl cl gl	pr fr br
sn sw cl	fl sl cl	fl sl gl	cr br fr
pr fr br	fl gl pr	cr sn sw	fl sl gl

28

Phonics

Name _____

Say the name of the picture.
Circle the blend you hear at the beginning of it.

sc st sp	pl bl sp	cr sc sp	sc sm sk
cr sc tr	bl pl tr	st tr sk	sk sp sc
st sk sp	pl bl st	sm sk sp	cr dr tr
dr tr cr	sc cr sm	dr tr bl	sc dr cr

29

Phonics

Circle the correct blend for each sentence.
Print it on the line.

1. The _____og sat in the pond.

2. I will play with my _____edge.

3. Brad's book is _____ue.

4. A _____ab is in the sand.

5. Jean likes to _____im in the lake.

6. We ate some _____apes.

7. A grey _____ake was in the grass.

30

Phonics

Circle the word for each picture.

	stale		clock		frog
	snail		flock		clog
	scale		smock		free

	glad		sledge		drain
	class		sped		dress
	glass		slip		press

	black		truck		smoke
	block		stuck		spoke
	broke		train		snake

	snake		grate		crab
	smoke		plate		crate
	skate		slate		clay

31

Phonics

wish	ship	shop
fish	shell	push
dish	wash	

Practise!

Fill in the blanks with words.

1	Here is your _____ of milk.
2	I caught a _____ !
3	I _____ I had a brother.
4	What a pretty _____ .
5	I got Rover at the pet _____ .

Phonics

Name _____

> **rich**   **chat**   **path**
>
> **chip**   **bath**   **thin**
>
> **chug**   **maths**

Fill in the blanks with words.

1	I'm taking a _____.
2	Let's _____.
3	I love to do _____.
4	I ate a potato _____ .
5	I am not _____.

33

Phonics

back	**tack**	**lick**
pack	**pick**	**sick**
sack	**kick**	

Fill in the blanks with words.

1	Have a _____, Pooch.
2	I feel _____.
3	I _____ this one.
4	I have a _____ of gum.
5	What is in the _____ ?

34

sing	ring	song
wing	bang	long
king	hang	

Fill in the blanks with words.

1 	We like to _____ .
2 	His nose is _____ .
3 	I am the_____ .
4 	I like your _____ .
5	She likes to _____ .

Phonics

Circle the word for each picture. Colour all the pictures.

	fad fan fat	 man map mat	 ham has hat
	bag bat back	 can cat cap	 bat bad bag
	cap cab can	 pat pad pan	 rag rat ram
	has ham hand	 lamp lad land	 sand sat sack

36

Phonics

Finish the word in the boat with the correct letter.
Then write the word.

37

Name _____

Write the word that goes with each picture. Use the word bank.

can	fan	man	pan
bat	sad	cat	pad
hat	rat	dad	tan

‗ ‗ ‗ ‗ ‗ ‗ ‗ ‗ ‗

Write the words you did not use here.

‗ ‗ ‗ ‗ ‗ ‗ ‗ ‗ ‗

38

Phonics

Name _____

Print the word for each picture. Colour the pictures.

_____ _ _ _ _ _ _ _ _____	_____ _ _ _ _ _ _ _ _____	_____ _ _ _ _ _ _ _ _____
_____ _ _ _ _ _ _ _ _____	_____ _ _ _ _ _ _ _ _____	_____ _ _ _ _ _ _ _ _____
_____ _ _ _ _ _ _ _ _____	_____ _ _ _ _ _ _ _ _____	_____ _ _ _ _ _ _ _ _____

Phonics

Draw the picture.

glad dad	**sad man**	**fat rat**
cat in a hat	**sad lad**	**rat on a cat**
fat man in a hat	**cat in a pan**	**rat on a can**

40

Choose words to put in the sentences.

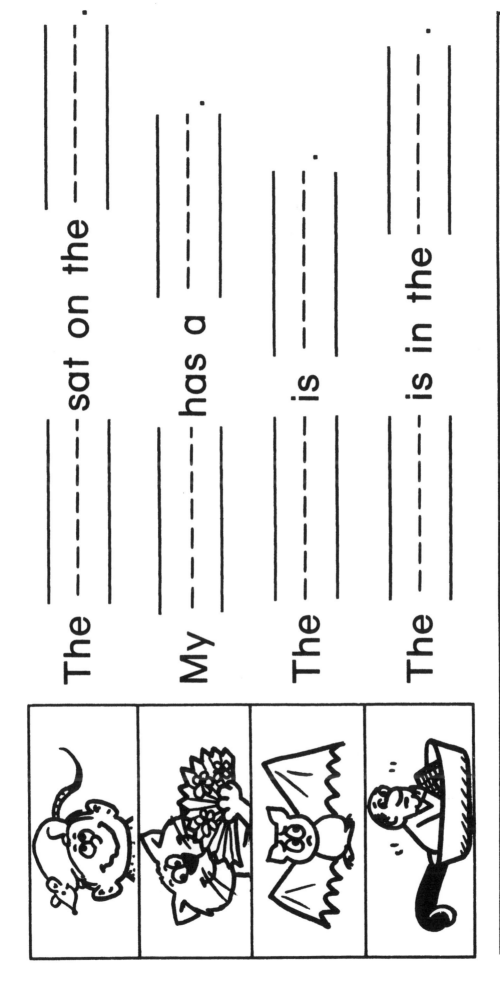

The ———— sat on the ————.

My ———— has a ————.

The ———— is ————.

The ———— is in the ————.

cat	rat	fan	lad	man	pan	sad	bat

41

Phonics

Write six words that rhyme and...one more if you can!

cat

1. _____
2. _____
3. _____
4. _____
5. _____
6. _____
☆ _____

man

1. _____
2. _____
3. _____
4. _____
5. _____
6. _____
☆ _____

sad

1. _____
2. _____
3. _____
4. _____
5. _____
6. _____
☆ _____

42

Phonics

Circle the word for each picture. Colour all the pictures.

bed bell bet	tell ten tent	web went west
jell jet jest	led let leg	net neck nest
hem hen help	bed beg bell	peg pen pet
nest net neck	tent tell test	neck net nest

43

Phonics

Finish the word in the boat with the correct letter.
Then write the word.

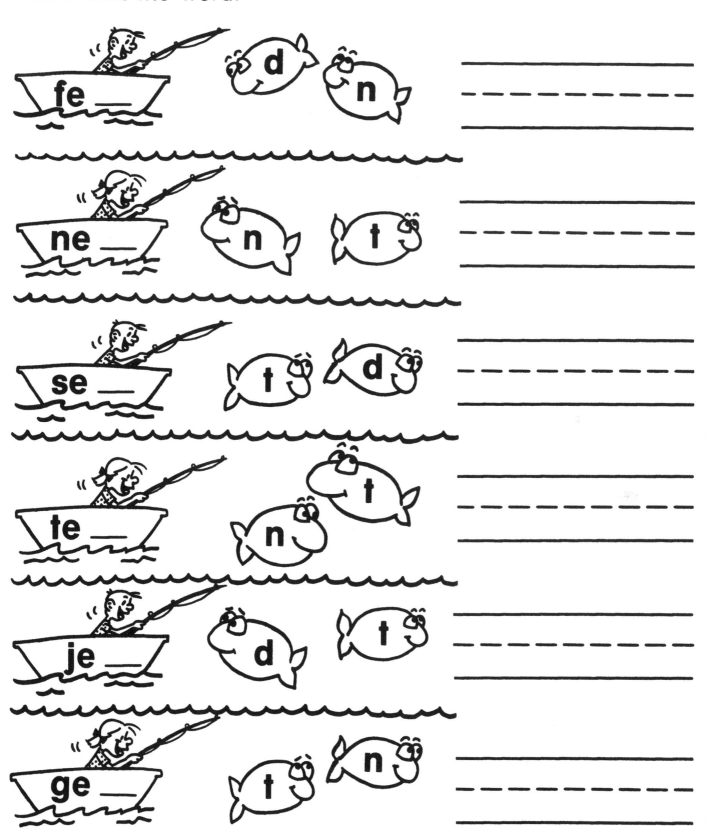

Phonics

Write the word that goes with each picture. Use the word bank.

jet	**bed**	**get**	**net**
Ted	**pet**	**hen**	**men**
pen	**ten**	**red**	**wet**

Write the words you did not use here.

_____   _____   _____

‑ ‑ ‑ ‑ ‑ ‑ ‑ ‑ ‑ ‑ ‑   ‑ ‑ ‑ ‑ ‑ ‑ ‑ ‑ ‑ ‑ ‑   ‑ ‑ ‑ ‑ ‑ ‑ ‑ ‑ ‑ ‑ ‑

_____   _____   _____

Print the word for each picture. Colour the pictures.

46

Phonics

Draw the picture.

red pen	**bed on a jet**	**hen in a net**
wet hen	**ten men**	**Ted and Ben**
pet in a pen	**ten wet men**	**Ben's den**

Phonics

Choose words to put in the sentences.

The _____ is in a _____.

The _____ the _____.

The _____ is on the _____.

The _____ is _____.

pen	Ben	hen	fed	pet	jet	net	wet	bed

48

Phonics

Write six words that rhyme and...one more if you can!

ten

1. _____
2. _____
3. _____
4. _____
5. _____
6. _____
☆ _____

net

1. _____
2. _____
3. _____
4. _____
5. _____
6. _____
☆ _____

red

1. _____
2. _____
3. _____
4. _____
5. _____
6. _____
☆ _____

49

Phonics

Circle the word for each picture. Colour all the pictures.

rip rib ring	sit six sick	pin pill pick
wig wing wick	mix mitt miss	hid hip hill
bib big bit	fit fill fish	pig pick pink
king kick kiss	lid lip lit	mill mink milk

50

Phonics

Name _____ Skill: Short vowel **i**

Finish the word in the boat with the correct letter.
Then write the word.

Phonics

Write the word that goes with each picture. Use the word bank.

fig	pit	big	dig
pig	wig	hip	tip
lit	hit	rip	lip

Write the words you did not use here.

_____   _____   _____

_ _ _ _ _ _ _ _   _ _ _ _ _ _ _ _   _ _ _ _ _ _ _ _

_____   _____   _____

Phonics

Print the word for each picture. Colour the pictures.

_____	_____	_____
_____	_____	_____

53

Phonics

Draw the picture.

big pig	**pig with a big lip**	**pig in a pit**
pig with a fig	**Sue bit a fig**	**pig with a wig**

54

Phonics

Choose words to put in the sentences.

The _ _ _ _ _ _ has a _ _ _ _ _ _.

Tim _ _ _ _ _ _ the _ _ _ _ _ _.

Sue can _ _ _ _ _ _ with her _ _ _ _ _ _.

Jim _ _ _ _ _ _ his _ _ _ _ _ _.

wig   bit   sip   fig   hit   lip   sip   pig   hip

Phonics

Skill: Short vowels **ig**, **ip**, **it**

Write six words that rhyme and...one more if you can!

pig

1. _____
2. _____
3. _____
4. _____
5. _____
6. _____

☆

hip

1. _____
2. _____
3. _____
4. _____
5. _____
6. _____

☆

sit

1. _____
2. _____
3. _____
4. _____
5. _____
6. _____

☆

Phonics

Name _____

Circle the word for each picture. Colour all the pictures.

bog box boss	dot dog doll
dot dog dock	fog for fox
pot pod pond	log lot lock
sob sock song	top tot toss

mop mob moss
rod rob rock
dog dot doll
lot log lost

57

Phonics

Finish the word in the boat with the correct letter.
Then write the word.

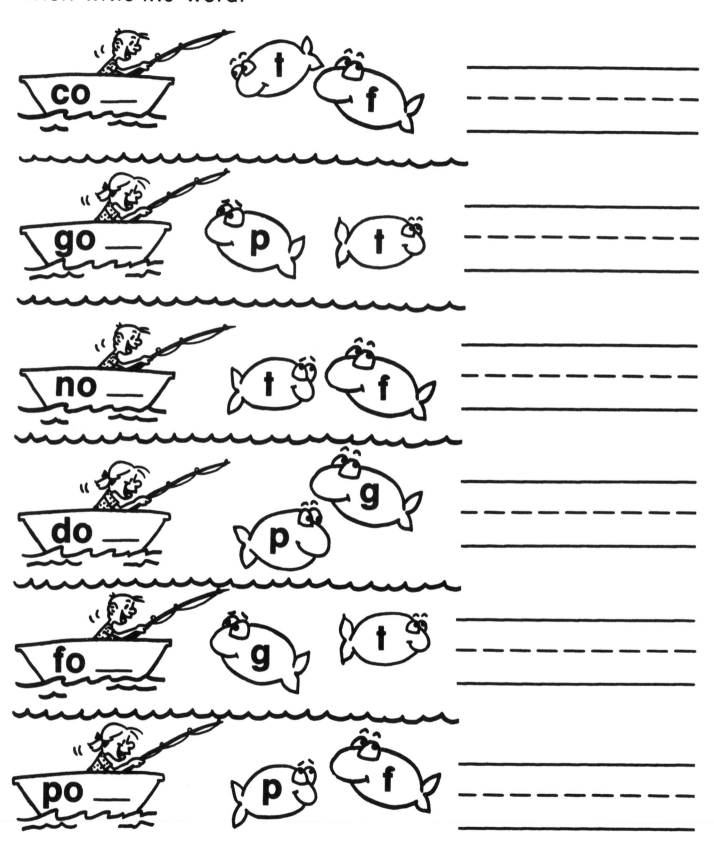

Phonics

Name _____

Write the word that goes with each picture. Use the word bank.

pop	**hop**	**mop**	**top**
hot	**dot**	**cot**	**pot**
dog	**jog**	**fog**	**log**

Write the words you did not use here.

_____ _____ _____

_____ _____ _____

59

Phonics

Skill: Short vowel **o**

Print the word for each picture. Colour the pictures.

Phonics

Skill: Short vowel **o**

Draw the picture.

dog with a mop	**dot on a dog**	**jog in the fog**
hot dog	**hog on a cot**	**hop over the log**
pot with a top	**dot on a pot**	**dog on a log**

Phonics

Name _____

Choose words to put in the sentences.

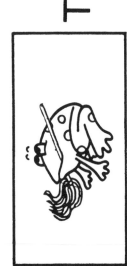

The _____ has a _____ .

The _____ has no _____ .

My _____ is on the _____ .

mop	frog	log	top	pot	cop	dog

Phonics

Skill: Short vowels **op**, **ot**, **og**

Write six words that rhyme and...one more if you can!

mop

1. ____
2. ____
3. ____
4. ____
5. ____
6. ____
☆

dot

1. ____
2. ____
3. ____
4. ____
5. ____
6. ____
☆

jog

1. ____
2. ____
3. ____
4. ____
5. ____
6. ____
☆

Phonics

Print the correct word for each sentence.

1. Dan will _____ a cake.
   back, bake

2. They are playing a _____ .
   game, gate

3. Tim has a _____ .
   pail, rail

4. May I have some _____ ?
   tap, tape

5. Jill was ill all _____ .
   day, date

6. It may _____ today.
   ran, rain

Phonics

Print the answer to each riddle on the correct flower.
Use the words in the beehive to help you.

1. Some birds live in me.

   1. _____

2. I live in the sea.

   2. _____

3. I help you to walk.

   3. _____

4. I am on a bird.

   4. _____

5. I can fly.

   5. _____

6. I am green.

   6. _____

Draw a path to show how the bee
will get home.

bee	tree
pea	beak
eel	feet

65

Phonics

Print the correct word for each picture.

1. Jane has a new _____ .
   bite, bike

2. I have _____ books.
   five, hive

3. Dad has a red _____ .
   time, tie

4. Dick played with his _____ .
   kite, kick

5. We will eat some _____ .
   pie, pile

6. It is _____ to get up.
   tile, time

Phonics

Print the correct word for each picture.

_____
1. The_____ is red.
rose, hose

2. That black pup is_____.
cut, cute

3. The_____ leaf is yellow.
oak, oar

4. The green_____ate a bug.
toe, toad

5. My new coat is_____.
blue, glue

6. The brown _____ is eating.
mule, rule

Colour the pictures to match the sentences.

67

Phonics

Fill in the missing vowel.

1. Five and four are n __ ne.

2. A dish is a pl __ te.

3. Let's take a r __ de.

4. This bike is m __ ne.

6. You can swim in the l __ ke.

7. This is the right s __ ze.

8. Let's sit in the sh __ de.

9. A clock tells the t __ me.

10. Is this a j __ ke?

68

Phonics

name	came	like
game	time	bike
same	cake	

Silent e

Fill in the blanks with words.

1 Ten pence, please.	The _____ costs ten pence.
2	What _____ is it?
3 I'm Polly	What is your _____ ?
4 Good idea.	Let's play a _____ .
5	You two look the _____ .

69

Phonics

Hmmm

Hmmmmm

Write the words in the correct order.

1. The cute is kitten.

_____

2. me the Give ice cube.

_____

3. Let's tune this hum.

_____

4. fast My runs mule.

_____

Circle all the long vowel u words.
Write the long vowel u words.

1. _____   3. _____

2. _____   4. _____

70

Circle the word for each picture.

sail say seal	pie pea pay	boat bone bait
robe read rope	got gate goat	cube cut cute
pail pay peel	tie tea toad	bay bee boat
tea tail toad	leaf lay load	ran rain road

71

Phonics

Print the correct word for each picture.

1. Mike has a blue _____.

                        oat, boat

2. He wants to _____ it.

                       seal, sail

3. He is going to the _____.

                       lake, leak

4. Mike _____ to go fast.

                 needs, seeds

5. He may not have _____ to play.

                    tie, time

6. It looks like _____ today.

                   ran, rain

Draw the rain coming down.
Colour the picture.

Phonics

Print the missing vowel.
Colour each picture that has the sound of a long vowel.

cr __ b	dr __ m	sl __ de
fr __ g	sn __ ke	tr __ e
sm __ ke	dr __ ss	pr __ ze
sk __ nk	bl __ ck	pl __ g

73

Phonics

Name _____

Print the correct word for each sentence.

1. Greg had a funny _____.
   dream, cream

2. He met a fish that had _____.
   lags, legs

3. The fish did not _____.
   skim, swim

4. Greg and the fish ate a _____.
   snack, slack

5. They sat under a _____.
   free, tree

6. They had a good _____.
   time, tame

Draw the dream that Greg had.

74

Phonics

Name _____ Skill: Short and long vowels,
Consonant blends

Use the Word Box to answer the riddles.

1. Some fish can live in me.

2. A baby sleeps in me.

3. I am good to eat.

4. I help you keep clean.

5. I make you wet.

6. Bees live in me.

7. I can jump and swim.

8. I blow up tyres.

What is the dragon saying?
To find out, print each
circled letter on
the correct line.

C ___ ___ ___ ___ ___
2   4   1   7   8   5

___ ___ !
3   6

75

Phonics

At Farmer Joe's Farm

Use the words on the barn to answer the riddles.

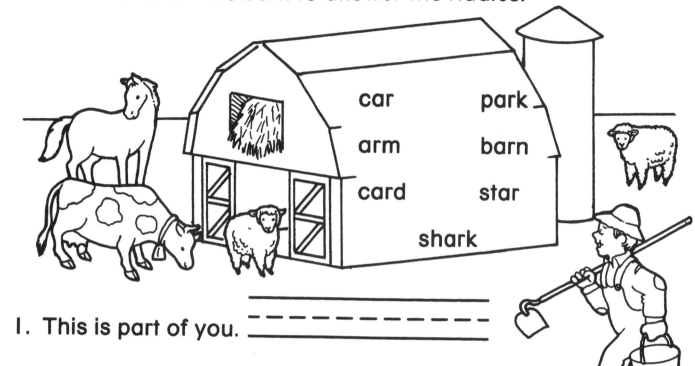

car   park

arm   barn

card   star

shark

1. This is part of you. _____

2. This has four tyres. _____

3. Farm animals can live here. _____

4. This is something in the sky. _____

5. Children can play here. _____

6. This is made from paper. _____

7. This animal lives in the sea. _____

76

Phonics

Ears of Corn

Write the correct word on each ear of corn.

1. Let's eat some _____ .
   horn   corn

2. Can I have some _____?
   more   store

3. This coat is too _____ for me.
   short   port

4. An ox has two _____ .
   horse   horns

5. I was _____ in June.
   born   torn

6. Baseball is a _____ .
   sport   store

7. We got wet in the _____ .
   stork   storm

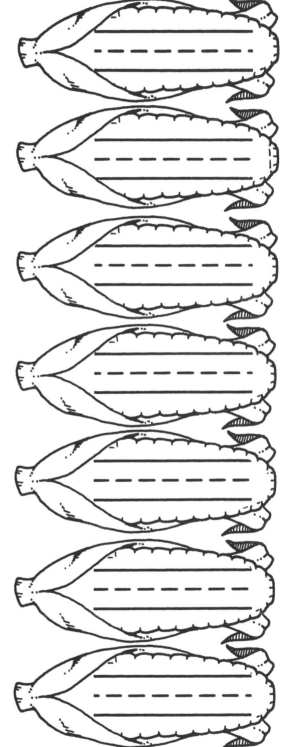

77

Phonics

Read Carefully

Circle the word for each picture.
Colour the pictures.

	cat car cord
	jab jar jay
	car card cord
	horn horse harm
	for far fork
	barn bark born
	card corn cord
	star store start
	for far forty
	arm art ark
	part park pork
	harp horn horse

Phonics

Ernie's Turn to Cross

Help Ernie Turtle cross the stepping stones
to get to the other side of the pond.

Write the name of the picture on each stone.
Use the words in the Word Box.

Word Box	
bird	nurse
girl	shirt
fern	curve
purse	mermaid

1. _ _ _ _ _ _ _ _ _

2. _ _ _ _ _ _ _ _ _

3. _ _ _ _ _ _ _ _ _

4. _ _ _ _ _ _ _ _ _

5. _ _ _ _ _ _ _ _ _

6. _ _ _ _ _ _ _ _ _

7. _ _ _ _ _ _ _ _ _

8. _ _ _ _ _ _ _ _ _

79

Phonics

Skill: **r-controlled vowels**

Watch the Letters!

Circle the word for each picture.
Colour the pictures.

bird born barn	far farm fork	car card cord
star stir store	mermaid sore harp	shirt short sharp
part purse port	hard hurt horn	tar turn turkey
corn card curb	stir skirt store	jar curve corner

80

Phonics

tail	nail	rain
jail	mail	pain
fail	pail	

Fill in the blanks with words.

1 	I love the _____.
2 	See my fuzzy _____?
3 	Fill the_____ with sand.
4 	Here is your _____.
5 	Hammer that _____.

81

Phonics

Write the words in the correct order.

1. for me Don't wait.

2. I brain with my think.

3. paid She bill the.

4. cat A has a tail.

Circle all the ai words.
Write the ai words.

1. _____   3. _____

2. _____   4. _____

82

Phonics

Write the words in the correct order.

1. Where tray is the?

_____
- -
_____

2. horse A hay eats.

_____
- -
_____

3. How pay I must much?

_____
- -
_____

4. Can I here stay?

_____
- -
_____

Circle all the ay words.
Write the ay words.

1. _____   3. _____

2. _____   4. _____

Phonics

Skill: **aw, au**

What Is It?

Use the words on Paul's list to answer the riddles.

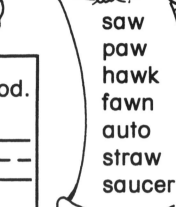

1. This is a car.

_____

saw
paw
hawk
fawn
auto
straw
saucer

2. This cuts wood.

_____

3. This is a cat's foot.

_____

4. This is a dish.

_____

5. This helps you drink.

_____

6. This is a bird.

_____

7. This is a baby deer.

_____

84

Phonics

Follow the Thread

Use the words on the spool of thread to complete each sentence.

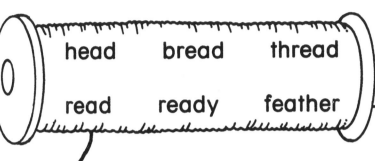

head   bread   thread

read   ready   feather

1. Dan will bake some _____ .

2. The class is _____ to go.

3. Pam had a hat on her _____ .

4. Last week I _____ a book.

5. I need some _____ to mend my coat.

6. The bird lost a _____ .

Phonics

Name _____

Dewey's Brew

Write the answers in the boxes.
Use the words in the Word Box.

Word Box

new

dew

blew

grew

flew

stew

1. We had ☐◯☐☐ for dinner.

2. The wind ☐◯☐☐ the leaves away.

3. I wore my ☐◯☐ coat.

4. The bird ☐☐☐◯ to the nest.

5. The tree ☐☐◯☐ very tall.

6. The grass was wet with ☐◯☐ .

What did Dewey put in his brew?
To find out, write each circled letter
on the correct line.

Dewey put in a __ __ __   __ __ __ .
              4 6 1   3 5 2

86

Phonics

Almost Home

Help the captain and his crew sail for home.
Write the correct word for each sentence.

1. I _____ some pictures.
   drew   chew

2. Let's get _____ to go.
   head   ready

3. The plane _____ above me.
   new   flew

4. We ate some _____ .
   bread   blew

5. I _____ the ball.
   threw   thread

6. The _____ became cold.
   ready   weather

87

Phonics

What's on the Coin?

Write the correct word for each picture.
Use the words on the piggy bank to help you.

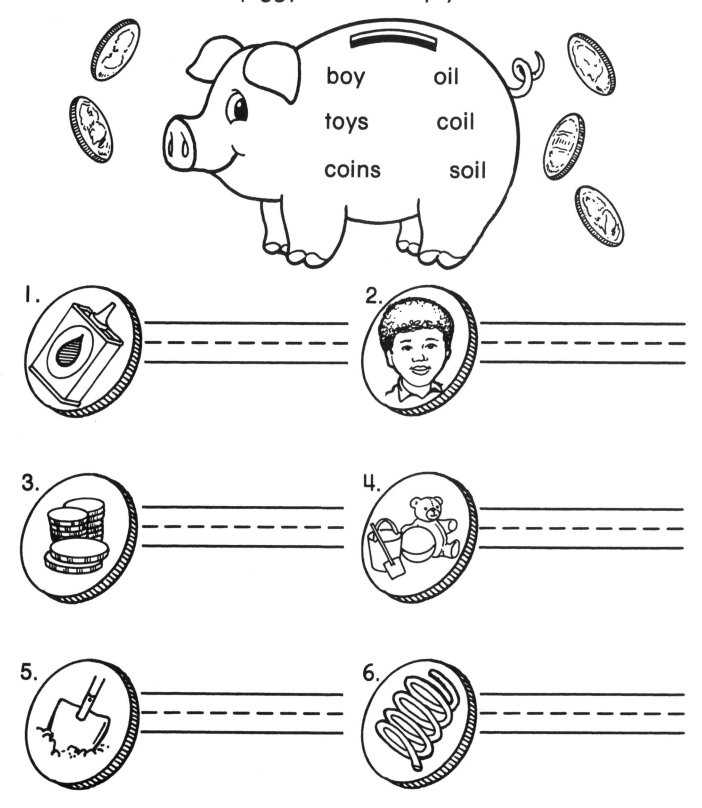

boy   oil

toys   coil

coins   soil

1. _ _ _ _ _ _ _ _ _ _ _

2. _ _ _ _ _ _ _ _ _ _ _

3. _ _ _ _ _ _ _ _ _ _ _

4. _ _ _ _ _ _ _ _ _ _ _

5. _ _ _ _ _ _ _ _ _ _ _

6. _ _ _ _ _ _ _ _ _ _ _

88

Can You Make the Right Choice?

Use the words from the word list to complete the sentences.

1. A 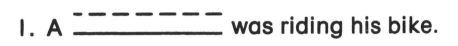 was riding his bike.

2. I will  some water.

3. Let's  the new club.

4. My 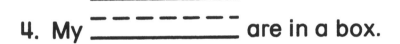 are in a box.

toys

boil

boy

soil

join

enjoy

point

5. This pencil has a sharp  .

6. Ken planted some seeds in the
_____ .

7. My friends and I 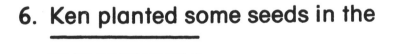 reading.

89

Phonics

Name _____

boy　　　pay　　　way
toy　　　day　　　may
joy　　　hay

Fill in the blanks with words.

1		See my new _____!
2		I am a _____.
3		Have a nice _____.
4		I eat _____ sometimes.
5		I will _____ five pence.

90

Phonics

In the Clouds

Write the correct word for each sentence.

1. Pam came to my _____ .
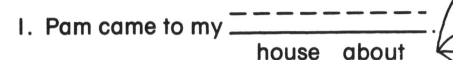
   house   about

2. We went _____ to play.
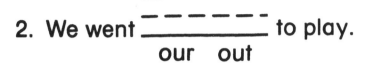
   our   out

3. We saw a _____ in the grass.
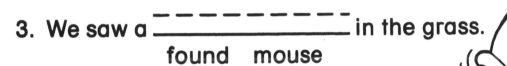
   found   mouse

4. Big, white _____ were in the sky.

   loud   clouds

5. Then I saw something big and _____ .

   sound   round

6. I _____ to Pam.
   scouted   shouted

7. Someone was high above the _____ !
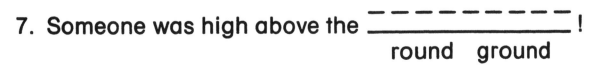
   round   ground

91

Phonics

Name _____

Read, Write, Colour

Write the correct word for each sentence.
Colour the pictures to match the sentences.

1. The _____ had a green hat.
   down   clown

2. That _____ is black and white.
   cow   how

3. A brown _____ sat in a tree.
   howl   owl

4. Sam picked a red _____.
   power   flower

5. Meg has a blue _____.
   town   gown

6. The king wore a yellow _____.
   crown   crowd

92

Phonics

low	cow	pow
row	how	wow
tow	now	

Look! The first three words sound different!

Fill in the blanks with words.

1	Ginger is my _____.
2	Please show me _____.
3	_____ the boat.
4	We had to _____ the car.
5	Look on the _____ shelf.

Phonics

Let It Snow!

Write the answers to the riddles on the snowballs.
Use the words on the snowman to help you.

1. This is a bird.

2. This is something that plants do.

3. This is white and falls from the sky.

4. This holds water.

5. This is a colour.

6. A room has this to bring in light.

7. You can do this to a ball.

snow

grow   throw

crow   window

bowl   yellow

94

Phonics

Know Your "OW" Sounds

Look at the words and numbers below.
Write the number of each word in the correct box.

1. cow	3. crow	5. crown	7. snow
2. owl	4. bowl	6. window	8. clown

Write the words from the Word Box in the columns below.

ow as in **down**

ow as in **grow**

Phonics

Name _____   Skill: **oo** (book) **oo** (food)

A Fish Story

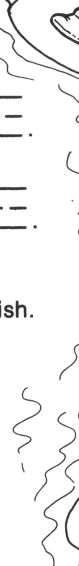

Write the correct word for each sentence.

1. Jan sat by a _____ .

   look   brook

2. She was fishing for _____ .

   food   hood

3. She got a fish on her _____ .

   hoof   hook

4. Jan wanted to _____ her fish.

   book   cook

5. She _____ out a pan.

   took   hook

6. She got _____ for a fire.

   wood   hood

7. Jan's dinner was _____ !

   foot   good

96

Phonics

> look   took   wood
> cook   hook   hood
> book   good

Fill in the blanks with words.

1	Dad is a good _____ !
2	This is a great _____ !
3	Who _____ my pie?
4	_____ at the bird!
5	This smells _____ !

97

       Phonics

Rocket to the Moon

Write the answer to each riddle on the rocket's pathway.
Use the words on the rocket to help you.

7. This is a bird.
_____
— — — — — — —
_____

6. You need to
eat this.
_____
— — — — — — — —
_____

5. You can swim in this.
_____
— — — — — — —
_____

4. This helps keep a room clean.

_____
— — — — — — — — — —
_____

3. This helps you to eat.

_____
— — — — — — — —
_____

2. Your teacher works here.
_____
— — — — — — — — —
_____

broom
food   spoon
school goose
pool   zoo

1. You can see
many animals here.

_____
— — — — — — —
_____

Phonics

"OO" Words

Circle the word for each picture.
Colour the pictures.

MOOSE
TALES

look / took / book	foot / food / hood	moo / moon / noon
moo / zoo / zoom	moose / loose / goose	hoof / hood / hook
cook / hook / hoof	boot / book / boom	spoon / spool / stool
broom / room / groom	spool / tool / stool	good / wool / wood

99

Phonics

Answer Key

Name _____

Skill Consonant blends **gl**
pl sl

Say the name of the picture.
Write the blend you hear at the beginning of it.

glove   plant   slide

sl	pl	gl	pl
gl	sl	pl	sl
gl	pl	gl	sl

Page 1

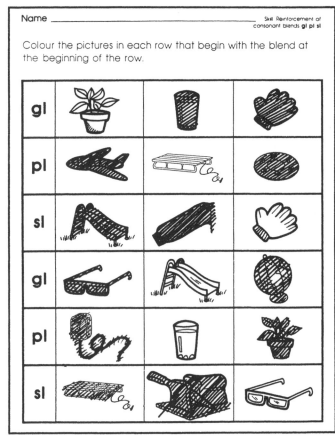

Name _____

Skill Reinforcement of
consonant blends **gl pl sl**

Colour the pictures in each row that begin with the blend at the beginning of the row.

gl			
pl			
sl			
gl			
pl			
sl			

Page 2

Name _____

Skill Consonant blends **bl**
cl fl

Say the name of the picture.
Write the blend you hear at the beginning of it.

block   clown   flower

bl	fl	cl	bl
bl	cl	fl	cl
cl	fl	bl	fl

Page 3

Name _____

Skill Reinforcement of
consonant blends **bl cl fl**

Colour the pictures in each row that begin with the blend at the beginning of the row.

bl			
cl			
fl			
bl			
cl			
fl			

Page 4

100

Phonics

Answer Key

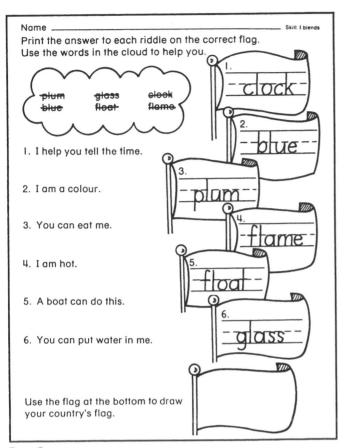

Page 5

Name _____ Skill: l blends

Print the answer to each riddle on the correct flag.
Use the words in the cloud to help you.

Cloud words: plum glass clock blue float flame

1. I help you tell the time.
2. I am a colour.
3. You can eat me.
4. I am hot.
5. A boat can do this.
6. You can put water in me.

Use the flag at the bottom to draw your country's flag.

Flags:
1. clock
2. blue
3. plum
4. flame
5. float
6. glass

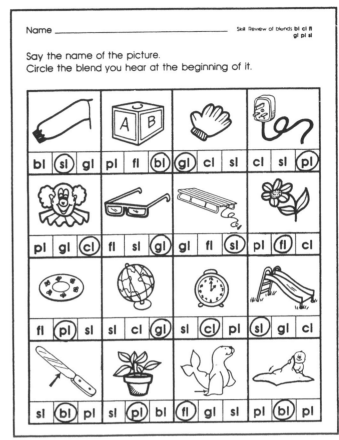

Page 6

Name _____ Skill: Review of blends bl cl fl gl pl sl

Say the name of the picture.
Circle the blend you hear at the beginning of it.

Row 1: bl (sl) gl | pl fl (bl) | (gl) cl sl | cl sl (pl)
Row 2: pl gl (cl) | fl sl (gl) | gl fl (sl) | pl (fl) cl
Row 3: fl (pl) sl | sl cl (gl) | sl (cl) pl | (sl) gl cl
Row 4: sl (bl) pl | sl (pl) bl | (fl) gl sl | pl (bl) pl

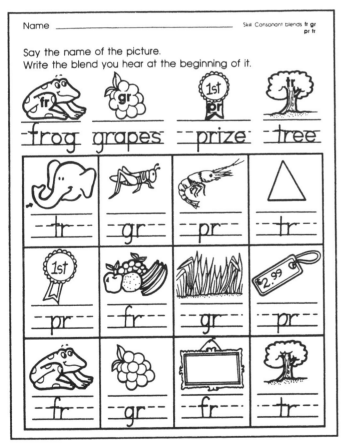

Page 7

Name _____ Skill: Consonant blends fr gr pr tr

Say the name of the picture.
Write the blend you hear at the beginning of it.

Examples: frog grapes prize tree

Row 1: tr | gr | pr | tr
Row 2: pr | fr | gr | pr
Row 3: fr | gr | fr | tr

Page 8

Name _____ Skill: Reinforcement of consonant blends fr gr pr tr

Colour the pictures in each row that begin with the blend at the beginning of the row.

fr
gr
pr
tr
gr
pr

101

Phonics

Answer Key

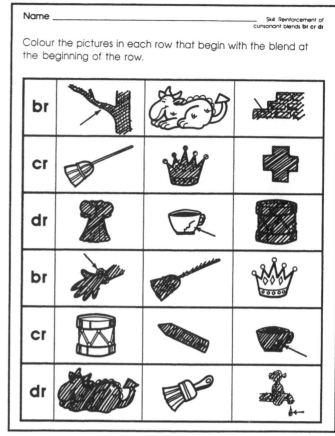

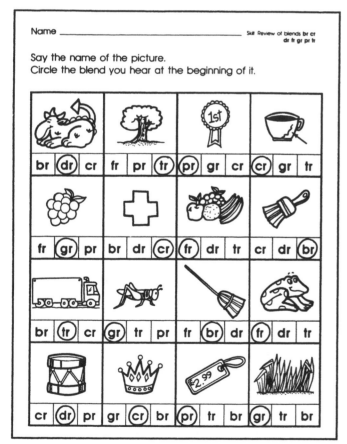

102

Phonics

Answer Key

Name _____

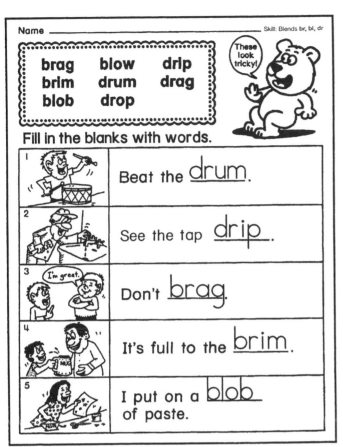

brag	blow	drip
brim	drum	drag
blob	drop	

Fill in the blanks with words.

1	Beat the <u>drum</u>.
2	See the tap <u>drip</u>.
3	Don't <u>brag</u>.
4	It's full to the <u>brim</u>.
5	I put on a <u>blob</u> of paste.

Page 13

Name _____

grin	glad	play
grip	glow	plum
grab	plug	

Fill in the blanks with words.

1	Let's <u>play</u> tag.
2	I will eat this <u>plum</u>.
3	Please <u>plug</u> it in.
4	Look at that cat <u>grin</u>.
5	I am <u>glad</u> you are here.

Page 14

Name _____

flag	frog	trip
flat	from	trim
flap	trap	

Fill in the blanks with words.

1	Now <u>flap</u> your wings.
2	Look out for the <u>frog</u>!
3	It's a letter <u>from</u> Grandma!
4	Look out for a <u>trap</u>.
5	This is our school <u>flag</u>.

Page 15

Name _____

clip	club	crib
clap	claw	crow
clam	crab	

Fill in the blanks with words.

	Suzy is in her <u>crib</u>.
2	Look at that <u>crow</u>.
3	I <u>clip</u> Max every month.
4	I found a <u>crab</u>.
5	Here is a <u>clam</u> shell.

Page 16

103

Phonics

Answer Key

Page 17

Page 18

Page 19

Page 20

104

Phonics

Answer Key

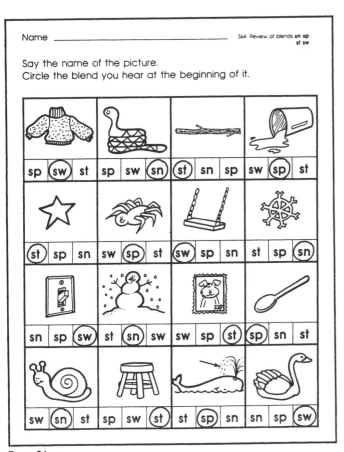

Name _____

Skill: Review of blends sn sp st sw

Say the name of the picture.
Circle the blend you hear at the beginning of it.

Page 21

Name _____

Skill: Consonant blends sk, sn, st

stir	snap	skip
stab	snug	skin
snip	snow	

Fill in the blanks with words.

1. I love the __snow__.
2. __Stir__ the batter.
3. I am __snug__ in bed.
4. __Snip__ a small piece off.
5. We like to __skip__.

Page 22

Name _____

Skill: Consonant blends sc sl sm

Say the name of the picture.
Write the blend you hear at the beginning of it.

scales   slide   smoke

Page 23

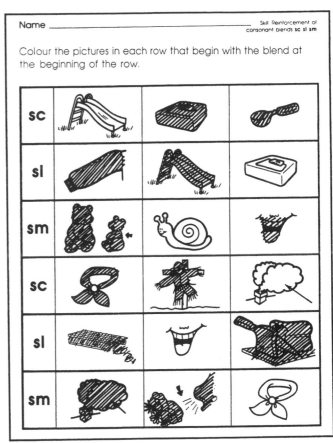

Name _____

Skill: Reinforcement of consonant blends sc sl sm

Colour the pictures in each row that begin with the blend at the beginning of the row.

sc			
sl			
sm			
sc			
sl			
sm			

Page 24

105

Phonics

Answer Key

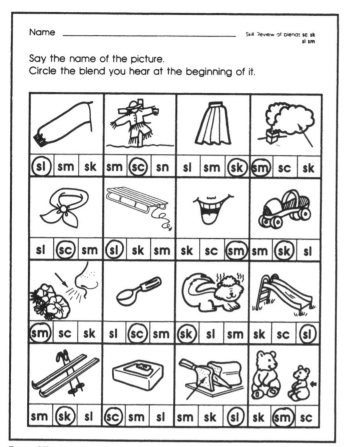

Page 25

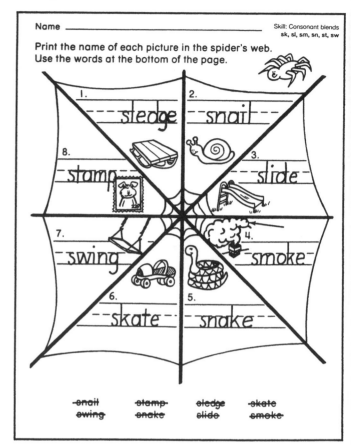

Page 26

Page 27

106

Phonics

Answer Key

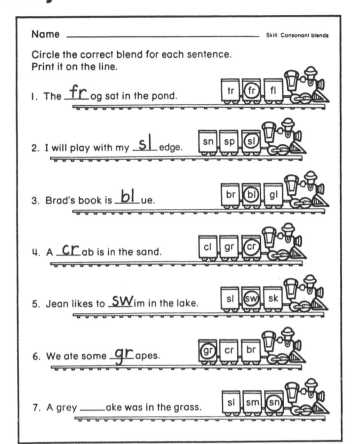

107

Phonics

Answer Key

Consonant blends
ch, th

| | rich   chat   path |
| chip   bath   thin |
| chug   maths |

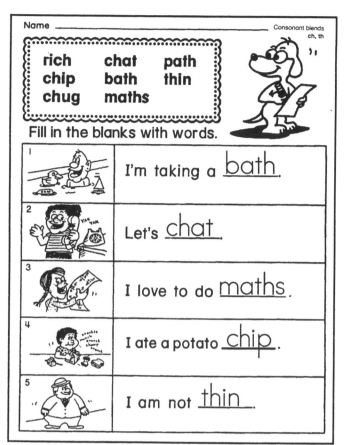

Fill in the blanks with words.

1	I'm taking a <u>bath</u>.
2	Let's <u>chat</u>.
3	I love to do <u>maths</u>.
4	I ate a potato <u>chip</u>.
5	I am not <u>thin</u>.

Page 33

Consonant blend ck

More words!

| back   tack   lick |
| pack   pick   sick |
| sack   kick |

Fill in the blanks with words.

1	Have a <u>lick</u>, Pooch.
2	I feel <u>sick</u>.
3	I <u>pick</u> this one.
4	I have a <u>pack</u> of gum.
5	What is in the <u>sack</u> ?

Page 34

Consonant blend ng

| sing   ring   song |
| wing   bang   long |
| king   hang |

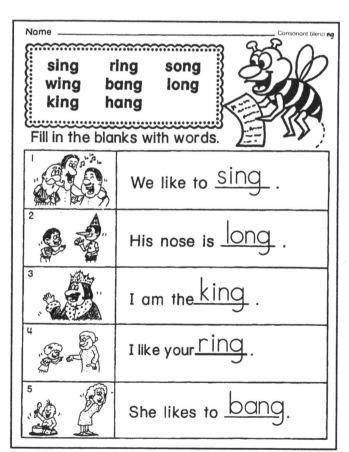

Fill in the blanks with words.

1	We like to <u>sing</u>.
2	His nose is <u>long</u>.
3	I am the <u>king</u>.
4	I like your <u>ring</u>.
5	She likes to <u>bang</u>.

Page 35

Skill: Short vowel a

Circle the word for each picture. Colour all the pictures.

fad		man		ham
(fan)		map		has
fat		mat		(hat)
(bag)		can		(bat)
bat		(cat)		bad
back		cap		bag
(cap)		pat		rag
cab		pad		(rat)
can		(pan)		ram
has		(lamp)		sand
ham		lad		sat
(hand)		land		(sack)

Page 36

108

Answer Key

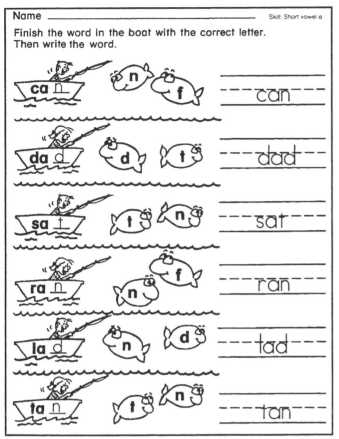

Page 37

Name _____ Skill: Short vowel a

Finish the word in the boat with the correct letter. Then write the word.

can

dad

sat

ran

tad

tan

Page 38

Name _____ Skill: Short vowel a

Write the word that goes with each picture. Use the word bank.

can	fan	man	pan
bat	sad	cat	pad
hat	rat	dad	tan

p a n	f a n	b a t
h a t	m a n	c a t
r a t	s a d	c a n

Write the words you did not use here.

dad   pad   fan

Page 39

Name _____ Skill: Short vowel a

Print the word for each picture. Colour the pictures.

can	bat	cap
lamp	man	axe
mat	cat	fan

Page 40

Name _____ Skill: Short vowel a

Draw the picture.

Pictures are drawn as directed.

glad dad	sad man	fat rat
cat in a hat	sad lad	rat on a cat
fat man in a hat	cat in a pan	rat on a can

109

Phonics

Answer Key

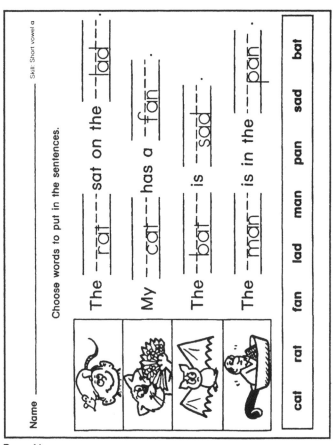

Page 41

Choose words to put in the sentences.

The __rat__ sat on the __lad__ .

My __cat__ has a __fan__ .

The __bat__ is __sad__ .

The __man__ is in the __pan__ .

| cat | rat | fan | lad | man | pan | sad | bat |

Name _____

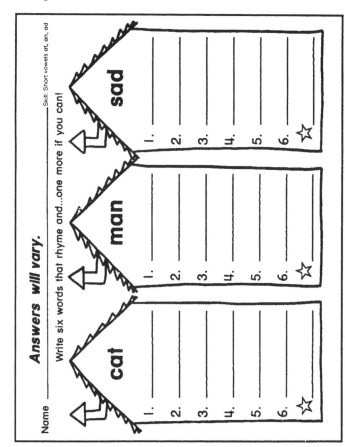

Page 42

Answers will vary.

Write six words that rhyme and...one more if you can!

sad

man

cat

1.
2.
3.
4.
5.
6. ☆

Name _____

Page 43

Name _____

Circle the word for each picture. Colour all the pictures.

	bed / bell / bet		tell / ten / tent		web / went / west
	jell / jet / jest		led / let / leg		net / neck / nest
	hem / hen / help		bed / beg / bell		peg / pen / pet
	nest / net / neck		tent / tell / test		neck / net / nest

Circled answers: bed, ten, web, jet, leg, net, hen, bell, pen, neck, tent, nest

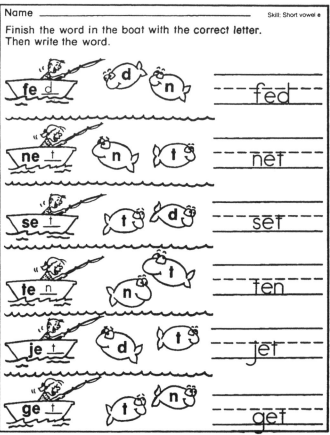

Page 44

Name _____

Finish the word in the boat with the **correct letter.**
Then write the word.

fe __d__   d n   __fed__

ne __t__   n t   __net__

se __t__   t d   __set__

te __n__   n t   __ten__

je __t__   d t   __jet__

ge __t__   t n   __get__

110

Phonics

Answer Key

Name _____   Skill: Short vowel e

Write the word that goes with each picture. Use the word bank.

jet	bed	get	net
Ted	pet	hen	men
pen	ten	red	wet

p e n   b e d   T e d

n e t   t e n   h e n

j e t   m e n   p e t

Write the words you did not use here.

get   red   wet

Page 45

Name _____   Skill: Short vowel e

Print the word for each picture. Colour the pictures.

ten   net   bed

pen   web   leg

bell   vest   tent

Page 46

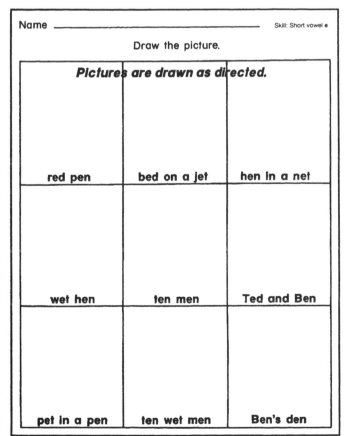

Name _____   Skill: Short vowel e

Draw the picture.

Pictures are drawn as directed.		
red pen	bed on a jet	hen in a net
wet hen	ten men	Ted and Ben
pet in a pen	ten wet men	Ben's den

Page 47

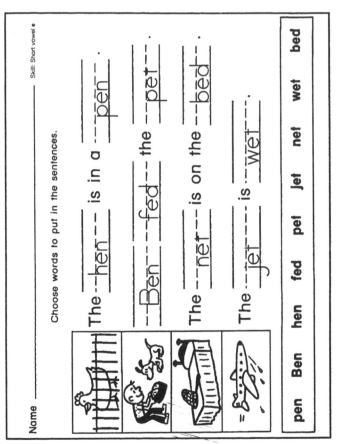

Skill: Short vowel e

Choose words to put in the sentences.

The hen is in a pen.

Ben fed the pet.

The net is on the bed.

The jet is wet.

| pen | Ben | hen | fed | pet | jet | net | wet | bed |

Page 48

111

Phonics

Answer Key

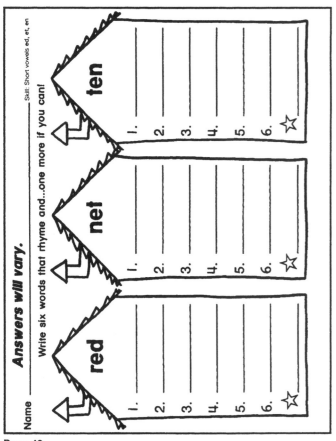

Page 49

Page 50

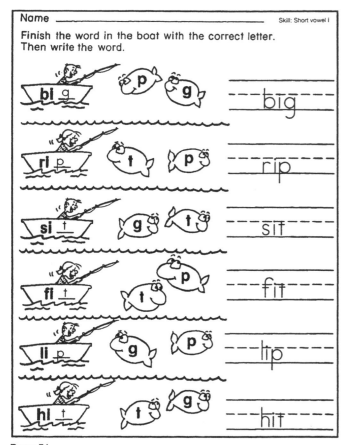

Page 51

Page 52

112

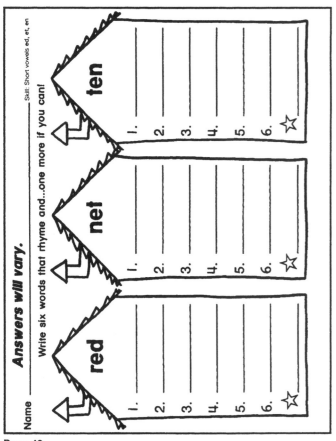

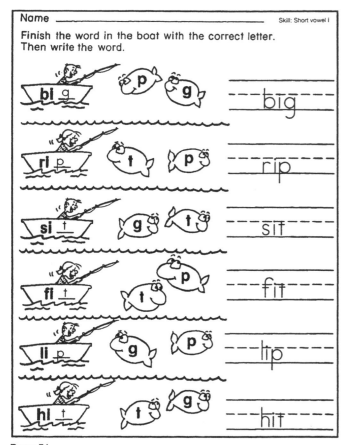

Phonics

Answer Key

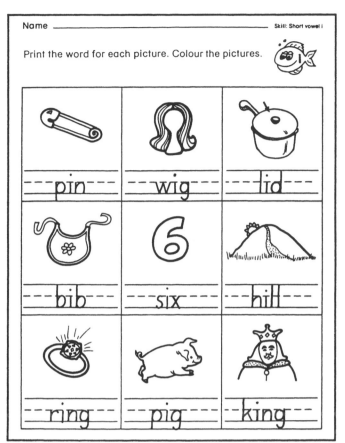

Print the word for each picture. Colour the pictures.

pin	wig	lid
bib	six	hill
ring	pig	king

Page 53

Draw the picture.

Pictures are drawn as directed.

big pig	pig with a big lip	pig in a pit
pig with a fig	Sue bit a fig.	pig with a wig

Page 54

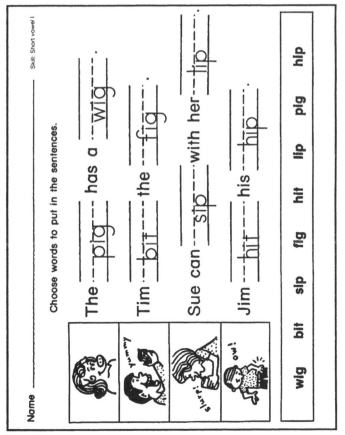

Choose words to put in the sentences.

The __pig__ has a __wig__.

Tim __bit__ the __fig__.

Sue can __sip__ with her __lip__.

Jim __hit__ his __hip__.

wig	bit	sip	fig	hit	lip	pig	hip

Page 55

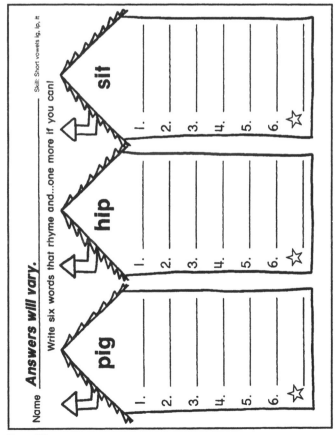

Answers will vary.

Write six words that rhyme and...one more if you can!

sit
1.
2.
3.
4.
5.
6. ☆

hip
1.
2.
3.
4.
5.
6. ☆

pig
1.
2.
3.
4.
5.
6. ☆

Page 56

113

Phonics

Answer Key

Circle the word for each picture. Colour all the pictures.

bog (box) boss	dot dog (doll)	(mop) mob moss
(dot) dog dock	fog for (fox)	rod rob (rock)
(pot) pod pond	log lot (lock)	(dog) dot doll
sob (sock) song	(top) tot toss	lot (log) lost

Page 57

Finish the word in the boat with the correct letter.
Then write the word.

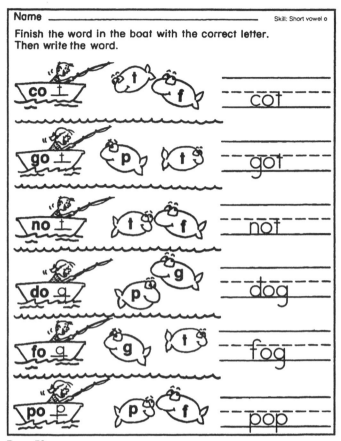

cot

got

not

dog

fog

pop

Page 58

Write the word that goes with each picture. Use the word bank.

pop	hop	mop	top
hot	dot	cot	pot
dog	jog	fog	log

p o t   m o p   d o g

h o p   t o p   l o g

c o t   j o g   d o t

Write the words you did not use here.

pop   hot   fog

Page 59

Print the word for each picture. Colour the pictures.

mop	pot	box
dot	top	lock
log	fox	sock

Page 60

114

Answer Key

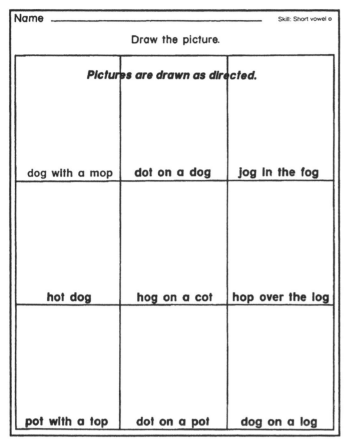

Page 61

Name _____ Skill: Short vowel o

Draw the picture.

Pictures are drawn as directed.		
dog with a mop	dot on a dog	jog in the fog
hot dog	hog on a cot	hop over the log
pot with a top	dot on a pot	dog on a log

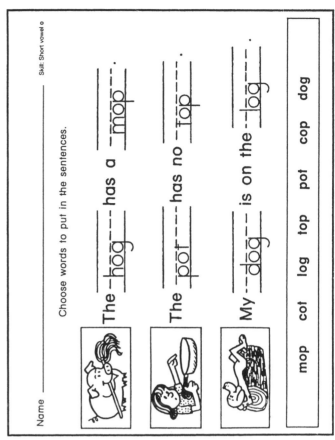

Page 62

Skill: Short vowel o

Name _____

Choose words to put in the sentences.

The hog has a mop.

The pot has no top.

My dog is on the log.

mop cot log top pot cop dog

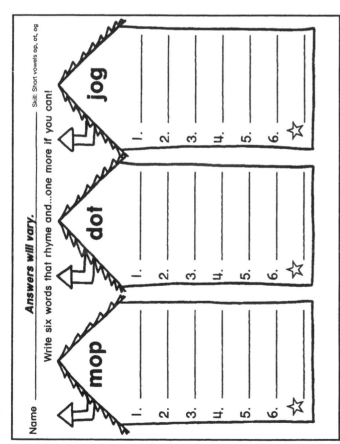

Page 63

Skill: Short vowels op, ot, og

Name _____

Answers will vary.

Write six words that rhyme and...one more if you can!

jog
1. 2. 3. 4. 5. 6. ☆

dot
1. 2. 3. 4. 5. 6. ☆

mop
1. 2. 3. 4. 5. 6. ☆

Page 64

Name _____ Skill: Long vowel a

Print the correct word for each sentence.

1. Dan will __bake__ a cake.
   back, bake

2. They are playing a __game__.
   game, gate

3. Tim has a __pail__.
   pail, rail

4. May I have some __tape__?
   tap, tape

5. Jill was ill all __day__.
   day, date

6. It may __rain__ today.
   ran, rain

115

Phonics

Answer Key

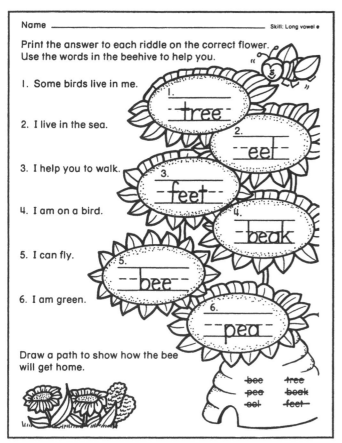

Print the correct word for each picture.

1. Jane has a new **bike**
   bite, bike

2. I have **five** books.
   five, hive

3. Dad has a red **tie**
   time, tie

4. Dick played with his **kite**
   kite, kick

5. We will eat some **pie**
   pie, pile

6. It is **time** to get up.
   tile, time

Fill in the missing vowel.

1. Five and four are n i ne.

2. A dish is a pl a te.

3. Let's take a r i de.

4. This bike is m i ne.

6. You can swim in the l a ke.

7. This is the right s i ze.

8. Let's sit in the sh a de.

9. A clock tells the t i me.

10. Is this a j o ke?

Answer Key

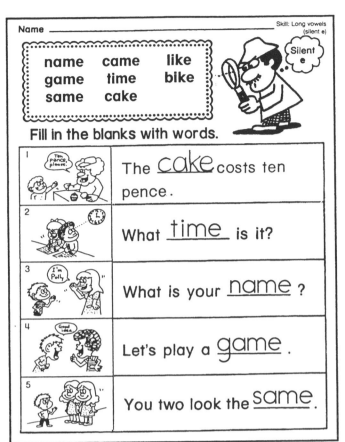

Skill: Long vowels (silent e)

Silent e

name	came	like
game	time	bike
same	cake	

Fill in the blanks with words.

1	The <u>cake</u> costs ten pence.
2	What <u>time</u> is it?
3	What is your <u>name</u> ?
4	Let's play a <u>game</u>.
5	You two look the <u>same</u>.

Page 69

Skill: Long vowel u words (silent e)

Hmmm ♪   Hmmmmm ♪

Write the words in the correct order.

1. The cute is kitten.

   <u>The kitten is (cute).</u>

2. me the Give ice cube.

   <u>Give me the ice (cube).</u>

3. Let's tune this hum.

   <u>Let's hum this (tune).</u>

4. fast My runs mule.

   <u>My (mule) runs fast.</u>

Circle all the long vowel u words.
Write the long vowel u words.

1. <u>cute</u>   3. <u>tune</u>

2. <u>cube</u>   4. <u>mule</u>

Page 70

Skill: Long vowels a, e, i, o, u

Circle the word for each picture.

sail / say / (seal)	(pie) / pea / pay	boat / (bone) / bait
robe / read / (rope)	got / gate / (goat)	(cube) / cut / cute
(pail) / pay / peel	(tie) / tea / toad	bay / (bee) / boat
tea / (tail) / toad	(leaf) / lay / load	ran / (rain) / road

Page 71

Skill: Long vowels a, e, i, o, u

Print the correct word for each picture.

1. Mike has a blue <u>boat</u>
   oat, boat

2. He wants to <u>sail</u> it.
   seal, sail

3. He is going to the <u>lake</u>.
   lake, leak

4. Mike <u>needs</u> to go fast.
   needs, seeds

5. He may not have <u>time</u> to play.
   tie, time

6. It looks like <u>rain</u> today.
   ran, rain

Draw the rain coming down.
Colour the picture.

Page 72

117

Phonics

Answer Key

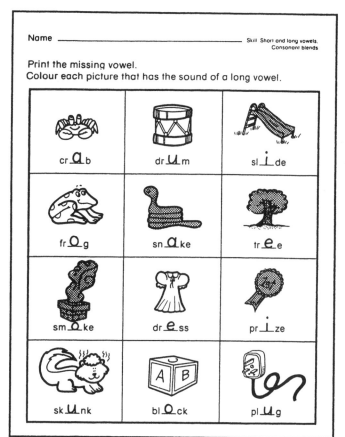

Name _____ Skill: Short and long vowels. Consonant blends

Print the missing vowel.
Colour each picture that has the sound of a long vowel.

cr **a** b	dr **u** m	sl **i** de
fr **o** g	sn **a** ke	tr **e** e
sm **o** ke	dr **e** ss	pr **i** ze
sk **u** nk	bl **o** ck	pl **u** g

Page 73

Name _____ Skill: Short and long vowels. Consonant blends

Print the correct word for each sentence.

1. Greg had a funny — dream —.
   dream, cream

2. He met a fish that had — legs —.
   lags, legs

3. The fish did not — swim —.
   skim, swim

4. Greg and the fish ate a — snack —.
   snack, slack

5. They sat under a — tree —.
   free, tree

6. They had a good — time —.
   time, tame

Draw the dream that Greg had.

Page 74

Name _____ Skill: Short and long vowels. Consonant blends

Use the Word Box to answer the riddles.

Word Box
~~crib~~
~~frog~~
~~pump~~
~~hive~~
~~lake~~
~~plum~~
~~rain~~
~~soap~~

1. Some fish can live in me. l a k e
2. A baby sleeps in me. c r i b
3. I am good to eat. p l u m
4. I help you keep clean. s o a p
5. I make you wet. r a i n
6. Bees live in me. h i v e
7. I can jump and swim. f r o g
8. I blow up tyres. p u m p

colour
2 4 1 7 8 5
me!
3 6

What is the dragon saying?
To find out, print each
circled letter on
the correct line.

Page 75

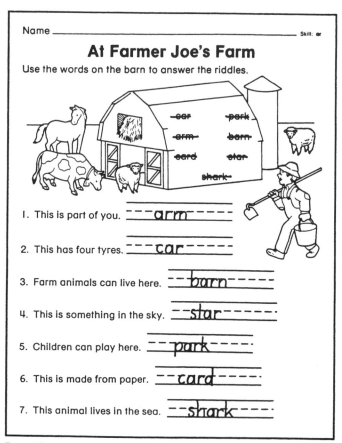

Name _____ Skill: ar

At Farmer Joe's Farm

Use the words on the barn to answer the riddles.

~~car~~   ~~park~~
~~arm~~   ~~barn~~
~~card~~   ~~star~~
~~shark~~

1. This is part of you. — arm —
2. This has four tyres. — car —
3. Farm animals can live here. — barn —
4. This is something in the sky. — star —
5. Children can play here. — park —
6. This is made from paper. — card —
7. This animal lives in the sea. — shark —

Page 76

118

Phonics

Answer Key

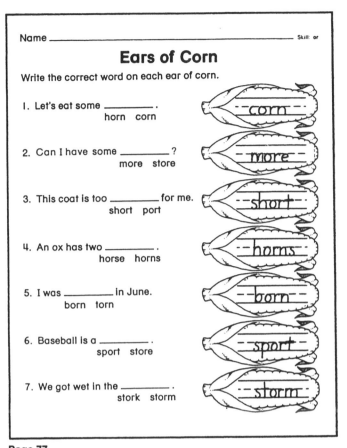

Name _____ Skill: or

Ears of Corn

Write the correct word on each ear of corn.

1. Let's eat some _____.
   horn   **corn**

2. Can I have some _____?
   more   store

3. This coat is too _____ for me.
   short   port

4. An ox has two _____.
   horse   **horns**

5. I was _____ in June.
   born   torn

6. Baseball is a _____.
   sport   store

7. We got wet in the _____.
   stork   **storm**

(ears of corn labeled: corn, more, short, horns, born, sport, storm)

Page 77

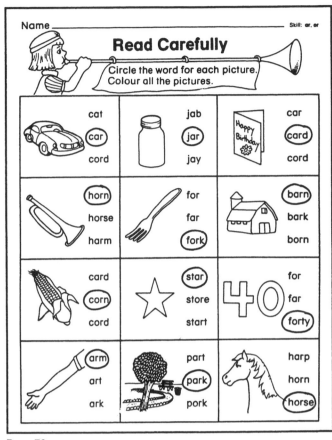

Name _____ Skill: ar, or

Read Carefully

Circle the word for each picture.
Colour all the pictures.

cat (car) cord	jab (jar) jay	car (card) cord
(horn) horse harm	for far (fork)	(barn) bark born
card (corn) cord	(star) store start	for far (forty)
(arm) art ark	part (park) pork	harp horn (horse)

Page 78

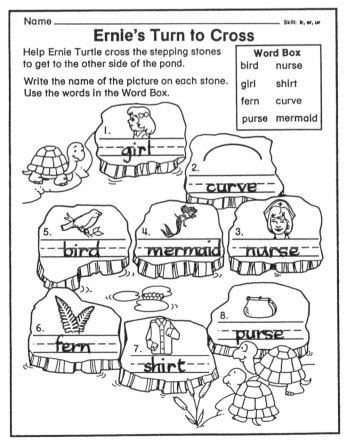

Name _____ Skill: ir, er, ur

Ernie's Turn to Cross

Help Ernie Turtle cross the stepping stones
to get to the other side of the pond.

Write the name of the picture on each stone.
Use the words in the Word Box.

Word Box
bird   nurse
girl   shirt
fern   curve
purse   mermaid

1. girl
2. curve
3. nurse
4. mermaid
5. bird
6. fern
7. shirt
8. purse

Page 79

Name _____ Skill: r-controlled vowels

Watch the Letters!

Circle the word for each picture.
Colour the pictures.

(bird) born barn	far farm (fork)	car (card) cord
(star) stir store	(mermaid) sore harp	(shirt) short sharp
part (purse) port	hard hurt (horn)	tar turn (turkey)
(corn) card curb	stir (skirt) store	jar (curve) corner

Page 80

119

Phonics

Answer Key

Name _____
Skill: Vowel digraphs ai

tall	nail	rain
jail	mail	pain
fail	pail	

Fill in the blanks with words.

1	I love the __rain__.
2	See my fuzzy __tail__?
3	Fill the __pail__ with sand.
4	Here is your __mail__.
5	Hammer that __nail__.

Page 81

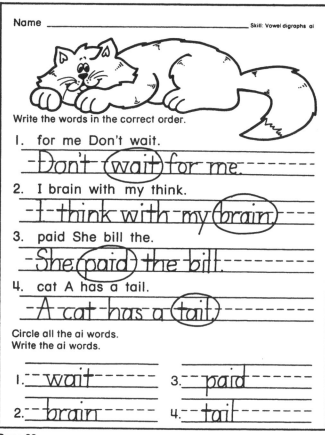

Name _____
Skill: Vowel digraphs ai

Write the words in the correct order.

1. for me Don't wait.
   __Don't (wait) for me.__

2. I brain with my think.
   __I think with my (brain)__

3. paid She bill the.
   __She (paid) the bill.__

4. cat A has a tail.
   __A cat has a (tail)__

Circle all the ai words.
Write the ai words.

1. __wait__   3. __paid__
2. __brain__   4. __tail__

Page 82

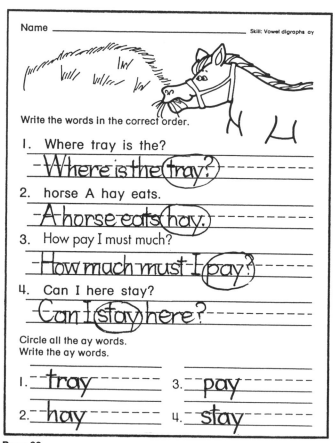

Name _____
Skill: Vowel digraphs ay

Write the words in the correct order.

1. Where tray is the?
   __Where is the (tray?)__

2. horse A hay eats.
   __A horse eats (hay.)__

3. How pay I must much?
   __How much must I (pay?)__

4. Can I here stay?
   __Can I (stay) here?__

Circle all the ay words.
Write the ay words.

1. __tray__   3. __pay__
2. __hay__   4. __stay__

Page 83

Name _____
Skill: aw, au

What Is It?

Use the words on Paul's list to answer the riddles.

~~saw~~
~~paw~~
~~hawk~~
~~fawn~~
~~auto~~
~~straw~~
~~saucer~~

1. This is a car.
   __auto__

2. This cuts wood.
   __saw__

3. This is a cat's foot.
   __paw__

4. This is a dish.
   __saucer__

5. This helps you drink.
   __straw__

6. This is a bird.
   __hawk__

7. This is a baby deer.
   __fawn__

Page 84

120

Phonics

Answer Key

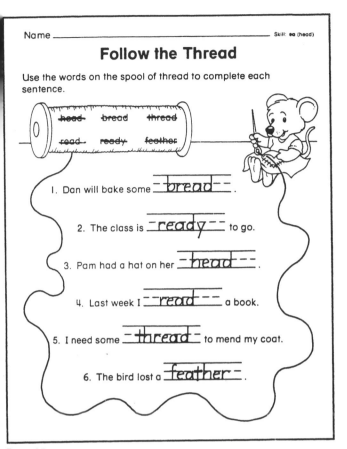

Follow the Thread

Use the words on the spool of thread to complete each sentence.

Word spool: head bread thread read ready feather

1. Dan will bake some **bread**.
2. The class is **ready** to go.
3. Pam had a hat on her **head**.
4. Last week I **read** a book.
5. I need some **thread** to mend my coat.
6. The bird lost a **feather**.

Skill: ea (head)

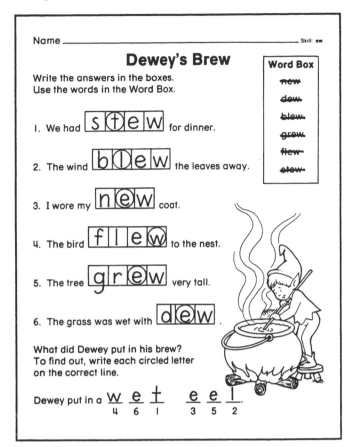

Dewey's Brew

Write the answers in the boxes.
Use the words in the Word Box.

Word Box
~~new~~
~~dew~~
~~blew~~
~~grew~~
~~flew~~
~~stew~~

1. We had s t(e)w for dinner.
2. The wind b(l)e w the leaves away.
3. I wore my n(e)w coat.
4. The bird f l e(w) to the nest.
5. The tree g r(e)w very tall.
6. The grass was wet with d(e)w.

What did Dewey put in his brew?
To find out, write each circled letter on the correct line.

Dewey put in a w e t   e e l .
                4 6 1   3 5 2

Skill: ew

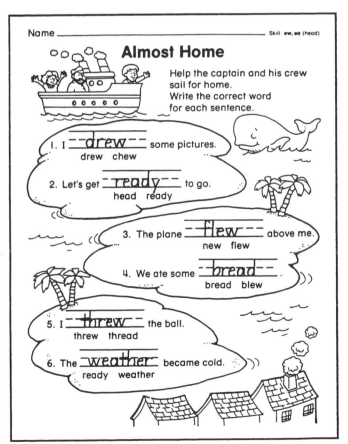

Almost Home

Help the captain and his crew sail for home.
Write the correct word for each sentence.

1. I **drew** some pictures.
   drew   chew
2. Let's get **ready** to go.
   head   ready
3. The plane **flew** above me.
   new   flew
4. We ate some **bread**.
   bread   blew
5. I **threw** the ball.
   threw   thread
6. The **weather** became cold.
   ready   weather

Skill: ew, ea (head)

What's on the Coin?

Write the correct word for each picture.
Use the words on the piggy bank to help you.

Piggy bank: ~~boy~~ ~~oil~~ ~~toys~~ ~~soil~~ ~~coins~~ ~~soil~~

1. **oil**
2. **boy**
3. **coins**
4. **toys**
5. **soil**
6. **coil**

Skill: oi, oy

121

Phonics

Answer Key

Can You Make the Right Choice?
Skill: oi, oy

Use the words from the word list to complete the sentences.

1. A __boy__ was riding his bike.

2. I will __boil__ some water.

3. Let's __join__ the new club.

4. My __toys__ are in a box.

5. This pencil has a sharp __point__.

6. Ken planted some seeds in the __soil__.

7. My friends and I __enjoy__ reading.

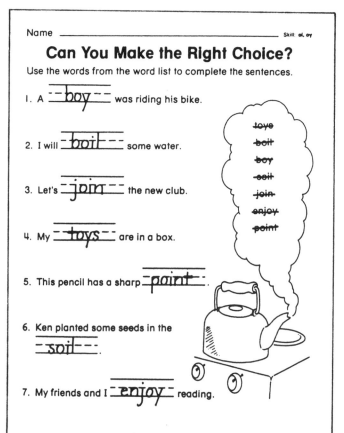

~~toye~~
~~boil~~
~~boy~~
~~soil~~
~~join~~
~~enjoy~~
~~point~~

Page 89

---

boy	pay	way
toy	day	may
joy	hay	

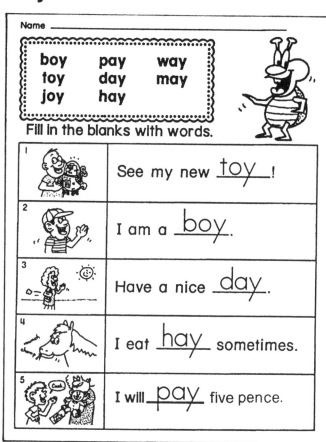

Fill in the blanks with words.

1	See my new __toy__ !
2	I am a __boy__.
3	Have a nice __day__.
4	I eat __hay__ sometimes.
5	I will __pay__ five pence.

Page 90

In the Clouds
Skill: ou (out)

Write the correct word for each sentence.

1. Pam came to my __house__.
   house   about

2. We went __out__ to play.
   our   out

3. We saw a __mouse__ in the grass.
   found   mouse

4. Big, white __clouds__ were in the sky.
   loud   clouds

5. Then I saw something big and __round__.
   sound   round

6. I __shouted__ to Pam.
   scouted   shouted

7. Someone was high above the __ground__ !
   round   ground

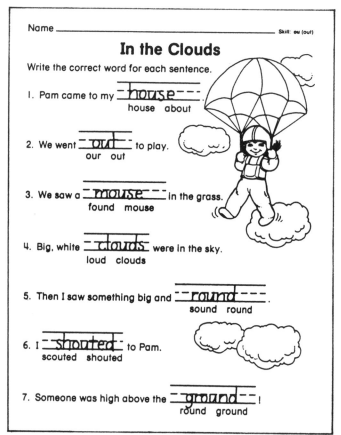

Page 91

Read, Write, Colour
Skill: ow (how)

Write the correct word for each sentence.
Colour the pictures to match the sentences.

1. The __clown__ had a green hat.
   down   clown

2. That __cow__ is black and white.
   cow   how

3. A brown __owl__ sat in a tree.
   howl   owl

4. Sam picked a red __flower__.
   power   flower

5. Meg has a blue __gown__.
   town   gown

6. The king wore a yellow __crown__.
   crown   crowd

Page 92

122

Phonics

Answer Key

Name _____ Skill: ow (now) ow (snow)

> Look! The first three words sound different!

low	cow	pow
row	how	wow
tow	now	

Fill in the blanks with words.

1		Ginger is my **cow**.
2		Please show me **how**.
3		**Row** the boat.
4		We had to **tow** the car.
5		Look on the **low** shelf.

Page 93

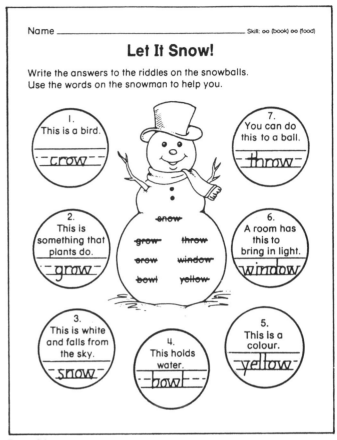

Name _____ Skill: oo (book) oo (food)

Let It Snow!

Write the answers to the riddles on the snowballs.
Use the words on the snowman to help you.

1. This is a bird. **crow**

2. This is something that plants do. **grow**

3. This is white and falls from the sky. **snow**

4. This holds water. **bowl**

5. This is a colour. **yellow**

6. A room has this to bring in light. **window**

7. You can do this to a ball. **throw**

Words on snowman: ~~snow~~ ~~grow~~ ~~throw~~ ~~crow~~ ~~window~~ ~~bowl~~ ~~yellow~~

Page 94

Name _____ Skill: ow (snow) ow (how)

Know Your "OW" Sounds

Look at the words and numbers below.
Write the number of each word in the correct box.

1. ~~cow~~	3. ~~crow~~	5. ~~crown~~	7. ~~snow~~
2. ~~owl~~	4. ~~bowl~~	6. ~~window~~	8. ~~clown~~

owl 2	cow 1	clown 8	bowl 4
snow 7	window 6	crow 3	crown 5

Write the words from the Word Box in the columns below.

ow as in down	ow as in grow
cow	crow
owl	bowl
crown	window
clown	snow

Page 95

Name _____ Skill: oo (book)

A Fish Story

Write the correct word for each sentence.

1. Jan sat by a **brook**. look brook

2. She was fishing for **food**. food hood

3. She got a fish on her **hook**. hoof hook

4. Jan wanted to **cook** her fish. book cook

5. She **took** out a pan. took hook

6. She got **wood** for a fire. wood hood

7. Jan's dinner was **good**! foot good

Page 96

123

Phonics

Answer Key

Skill: oo (book)

look	took	wood
cook	hook	hood
book	good	

Fill in the blanks with words.

1		Dad is a good <u>cook</u> !
2		This is a great <u>book</u> !
3		Who <u>took</u> my pie?
4		<u>Look</u> at the bird!
5		This smells <u>good</u> !

Page 97

Skill: oo (moon)

Rocket to the Moon

Write the answer to each riddle on the rocket's pathway.
Use the words on the rocket to help you.

7. This is a bird.
<u>goose</u>

6. You need to eat this.
<u>food</u>

5. You can swim in this.
<u>pool</u>

4. This helps keep a room clean.
<u>broom</u>

3. This helps you to eat.
<u>spoon</u>

2. Your teacher works here.
<u>school</u>

1. You can see many animals here.
<u>zoo</u>

food ~~broom~~
~~school~~ ~~spoon~~
~~pool~~ ~~goose~~
~~zoo~~

Page 98

Skill: oo (moon), oo

"OO" Words

Circle the word for each picture.
Colour the pictures.

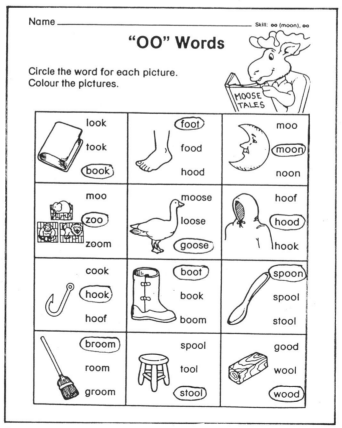

MOOSE TALES

look took (book)	(foot) food hood	moo (moon) noon
moo (zoo) zoom	moose loose (goose)	hoof (hood) hook
cook (hook) hoof	(boot) book boom	(spoon) spool stool
(broom) room groom	spool tool (stool)	good wool (wood)

Page 99

124

Phonics